POCAHONTAS

Colleen Reece

Illustrated by
Tim Holtrop

BARBOUR
PUBLISHING, INC.
Uhrichsville, Ohio

Published by Barbour Publishing, Inc.
        P.O. Box 719
        Uhrichsville, Ohio 44683
        http://www.barbourbooks.com

 Member of the
Evangelical Christian
Publishers Association

Printed in the United States of America.

AUTHOR'S NOTE
Concerning Pocahontas

In researching for this book, I discovered historians have a variety of opinions about the Indian maiden, Pocahontas: her date of birth, her first marriage, details of her association with the English settlers, and so on. This is especially true concerning the story of her saving Captain John Smith, leader of the settlers, from her father Chief Powhatan's wrath.

I chose to include the story or legend primarily because Captain Smith recounted it in his book, *True Relation of Virginia.** Such incidents did occur in the settling of America.

---

*Not in the earliest edition.

NONE WAS AS MIGHTY AS CHIEF POWHATAN.

1
Powhatan, Mighty Chieftain

Of all the Indian chiefs who had gathered in council, none was so mighty as Wahunsonacock,* Algonquian chieftain from the village of Werowocomoco. He sat high on a pile of mats, arms and moccasin-clad feet crossed. Keen, black eyes shone beneath his coarse, black hair. Sweat glistened on his bronze skin—bare beneath his animal skin robe except for a loincloth and broad bracelets on his powerful arms.

Chiefs from thirty Indian groups from mid-eastern North America formed a circle around Chief Powhatan. They came from different tribes: the Potomac and Chickahominy, the Rappahannock,

---

*He was also called Chief Powhatan, after his favorite village on the north banks of the James River, just east of what is now Richmond, Virginia. "Powhatan" means "falls of the river."

Pamunkey, and many others. They represented more than 200 Indian villages.

"Why have you summoned us?" Opechancanough demanded sullenly. His fierce face and dark scowl showed his love for war.

Powhatan gave his brother a haughty look. "We have many enemies." Heads nodded. The late 1500s were filled with skirmishes and raids by neighboring unfriendly tribes. Many there wore battle scars on their brown skins.

Powhatan continued. "I have prayed much to the Great Hare, our creator. I believe we must form an alliance to protect ourselves and our families."

Blank stares greeted him. Surprise showed on a few faces. Some looked thoughtful. Opechancanough scowled even more. "Are we sheep who must huddle together for protection? Pah!" He raised a brawny fist. "I say fight all who threaten us."

A slight murmur ran through the group but

"I SAY FIGHT ALL WHO THREATEN US."

Powhatan hadn't finished. "My brother, is not a bundle of sticks far stronger than one?" He snatched a slender stick from the ground beside him and broke it with a single snap of his fingers. "Banding together is not weakness, but strength."

"Powhatan is right," an aged Rappahannock chieftain said. Others agreed. Before the council ended, the Powhatan Confederacy had been formed.

"Now we must feast," Powhatan declared. He clapped his hands sharply. Squaws and maidens ran from the houses made of saplings lashed together and covered with bark. Powhatan ordered them to bring food and set it before their guests. Squash, potatoes, beans, and maize (corn) appeared, along with roasted venison and fish, wild turkey, nuts, and berries. Village dogs snarled and fought for the meat scraps tossed to them when the men could eat no more.

Opechancanough refused to rejoice over the new alliance. He wolfed down his food and stayed with

"NOW WE MUST FEAST," POWHATAN DECLARED.

the group only because not doing so would be to insult the other chiefs. He could not afford to do that. One day he might have need of them.

One by one the Indian chieftains rode off or slipped away from Werowocomoco on moccasined feet. At last, Powhatan entered his house, which was largest in the village since he was chief.

An Indian woman greeted him. "My husband, although the sun has gone behind the trees, still it shines in your face. What means this?"

Powhatan smiled into her eager, dark eyes. "Peace has come to the Powhatans, and I am glad."

Time passed. The Powhatan Confederacy remained in force and included almost 9,000 Indians. Hostile forces remained outside the Confederacy, but those chiefs who had pledged their tribes for the common good of all kept their vows.

Season followed season, and one day, Powhatan's wife presented him with a new daughter. They named

"PEACE HAS COME TO THE POWHATANS. . . ."

her Matowaka. The newborn kicked bare legs and waved her little brown arms.

Powhatan grunted approval. "This daughter of Powhatan is a playful one." He chuckled low in his throat. "She shall be known as Pocahontas."* She soon became her father's favorite. As she grew, Powhatan often told her she meant more to him than his own life.

Pocahontas lived a free and happy life. She tumbled with the other children in tall grass under tall trees. She gazed into blue skies and stained her fingers red with the juice of berries. Long practice made her fleet as the deer in the forest and nothing pleased her father more than to see his daughter challenge, and sometimes beat, others in foot races.

Her respect for the animal spirits her tribe worshiped, especially the Great Hare which they believed was their creator, filled her with a great love for raccoons and rabbits, squirrels, and singing birds. She

---

*Meaning "playful one."

"SHE SHALL BE POCAHONTAS, THE PLAYFUL ONE."

did not like opossums with their snarling snouts. She secretly thought her father's brother, Opechancanough, looked like an opossum. She shivered and avoided him as much as possible.

In every way Pocahontas lived up to her name. She grew as tall and straight as a sapling. Her curious mind wondered about everything. Where did the sun go when it winked goodnight to her and disappeared? Did it sleep, too? Perhaps. Sometimes when it rose in the east, she thought the sun yawned and stretched itself awake before shining down on her. Why did the stars not shine in the daytime? Were they night people, like the creatures that hid during the day and came out at dusk to feed and play?

Pocahontas loved the rivers and streams. They cooled her body on hot days, and she loved to splash in their tickling waters. Her settlement, of about fifty sapling and bark dwellings, offered companionship and an outlet for her energy. Not all was play. Even

POCAHONTAS LOVED THE RIVERS AND STREAMS.

small maidens were taught simple tasks that grew harder as the girls got older. Everyone in the village must work in order for the tribe to survive. The Indians cleared land, built houses, and farmed the land. They built canoes, made clothing, wove baskets, and did many other things necessary to their lives.

"Mother," Pocahontas said one day, "I wish I could be a wampum maker always." Her nimble fingers worked with white and purple beads made from the shells of sea creatures. "They are so pretty!" She held up a necklace.

"You do well, my child, but you must learn all the tasks if you are to one day be a good wife and mother."

"Like you?"

The mother's hands stilled for a moment then she went on weaving strands in and out, in and out, to create yet another basket. A lovely light came to her eyes. "Much better, I pray."

The comment sidetracked Pocahontas. "Mother,"

"I WISH I COULD BE A WAMPUM MAKER ALWAYS."

she asked, "wouldn't it be wonderful if when we pray, the Great Hare and animal spirits we pray to would reply?" Her eyes took on a dreaming look.

Her mother dropped her basket, but smiled indulgently. "You are fanciful, my daughter."

"But, why? Is it not rude to give no answer when someone speaks to you?"

Fear sprang to the older woman's face. "Hush, child. You must not say such things." She cast a fearful glance around to make sure they could not be overheard. "When one is young, one has many questions. You will forget them as you grow older."

Pocahontas rebelliously thought, *I do not want to forget them! I want to know all kinds of things,* but she wisely held her tongue. When Mother spoke in that tone of voice, it meant she expected obedience.

The very next morning, however, Pocahontas remembered. Her village rose at dawn as usual and welcomed the sun when it came. They scattered

"HUSH, CHILD. YOU MUST NOT SAY SUCH THINGS."

sacred tobacco from the plants they grew, lifted up their hands, and sang as their ancestors had done. Pocahontas knew they must never forget the god whose hands dripped with danger. Did he not send lightning bolts on those who mocked him, as well as flood, war, and drought? Yet the same god had made tiny, blooming flowers and birds whose calls roused her each morning. She sighed and whispered, "It is hard to understand."

With each passing season, Pocahontas wondered more. She hovered between childhood and maidenhood, impatient to be part of the dance of the unmarried girls. The day arrived. Never had she felt more alive than when she at last could join all the unmarried girls in her village in their dance. They clapped their hands and spun around, all noisy and happy. How wonderful it felt, to move like the very wind that sang, or stormed, through the trees near the village!

Pocahontas saw her father watching. She whirled

NEVER HAD POCAHONTAS FELT MORE ALIVE....

faster and leaped higher. Powhatan could no more keep his pride from showing than he could stop the rain. At last, the dance ended, but Pocahontas could not still her energized spirits. She challenged the others to a race. Laughing and shouting, they pelted over forest trails, beside the stream, and across the meadows. Pocahontas led them all. Her excited trill of laughter floated over one shoulder.

A cry of pain halted her flight. Pocahontas stopped so suddenly the maiden close behind her leaped aside to keep from hitting her. "Now I'll win," the girl boasted in a loud voice.

"It matters not," Pocahontas called after her. "Matachanna has fallen." She raced back to her sister.

"Is she hurt?" the girl called, poised to take off should the race continue.

Matachanna sat rubbing one foot.

"Can you walk?" Pocahontas asked.

POCAHONTAS CHALLENGED THE OTHERS TO A RACE.

"If you help me." She struggled up and leaned on her sister. They started toward the village. The other girls clustered around them, even the one who had wanted to win so badly. All offered to help, but Pocahontas said proudly, "I am her sister. I will take her to my mother, who will apply herbs and bind her foot."

"One day I will care for you," Matachanna promised. She giggled. "But not until I no longer hop on one foot with the other in the air like a long-legged marsh bird fishing for his supper!"

"ONE DAY I WILL CARE FOR YOU," MATACHANNA PROMISED.

THE DARING SIR WALTER RALEIGH

2

The Brave Ones

Thousands of miles across the ocean from the New World,* where Powhatan formed his confederacy long before Pocahontas was born, Elizabeth the Great ruled England. Daring Sir Walter Raleigh served as Captain of the Queen's Guard and yearned to plant English settlements in America. European kings were already claiming the country.

Anyone could stake a claim, but holding the land was another matter. It meant equipping large, strong ships and hiring sailors at high prices because of the danger. There had to be food for the round trip and also enough to keep the settlers for the year or more it took to clear land and raise crops.

Sir Walter Raleigh sailed to the New World several

*Known today as America.

times, but Queen Elizabeth did not want one of her favorites to drown. She made up reasons to keep him in England, so he sent others in his place.

Raleigh had grown rich from his capture of Spanish treasure. He had worked hard and found men who were willing to settle America, after two sea captains explored the American coast north of Florida. One, Arthur Barlowe, sent an exciting report of the New World. He named the entire country Virginia after Elizabeth, the Virgin Queen. Unfortunately, Raleigh's first group nearly starved to death. Sir Francis Drake rescued them and returned them to England.

Two years later, a second group set out. This time, a few brave women and children sailed with the men. John White served as governor. An artist, he'd come back with many water colors of the countryside from an earlier expedition.

"There's a wonderful place for a settlement," he told his fellow passengers. "Roanoke Island lies off

RALEIGH'S FIRST GROUP NEARLY STARVED TO DEATH.

the coast on a sound. It's twelve miles long and three to four miles wide. Ships can anchor near it and the narrow inlets can be guarded against Spanish raiding ships on one side." His eyes gleamed with anticipation. "There are several miles of water between it and the mainland on the other side. Unfriendly natives can only reach it by canoe."

Those who sailed with John White never tired of hearing how gigantic trees, wild grapes, raccoons the size of foxes, and abundant flowers made it ideal for their settlement. Alas for their dreams! All too soon John White realized they had brought far too few supplies. He must return to England and bring food or the 117 colonists would die of starvation.

"I can hardly bear to leave you," White told his daughter, Eleanor, who had married Ananias Dare, a colonist. White touched his new granddaughter's smooth cheek. "Little Virginia is only nine days old."*

---

*Virginia, born August 18, 1587, was the first English child born in America.

ALAS FOR THEIR DREAMS! HE MUST RETURN TO ENGLAND.

Yet he had no choice. He sadly sailed back to England, leaving his family on Roanoke Island.

John White reached England and found chaos! The country was preparing for an invasion by the Spaniards. Not a single ship could be spared. He could not return to America.

An entire year went by before the fleet of Spanish warships came. A week of terrible fighting was followed by months of chasing the Spaniards and cleaning up the wreckage. John White raged and feared. What fate had befallen those he had left in America more than two years earlier? He dreaded finding out.

John White had no way of knowing he was on the edge of one of the greatest mysteries in the history of America! In all his wildest imaginings, White could not have suspected what awaited him on Roanoke Island. His ship at last dropped anchor, and he went ashore. Fort Raleigh, as the settlers had named their little community, lay empty. The rude houses, pro-

JOHN WHITE REACHED ENGLAND AND FOUND CHAOS!

tected by a fence of pointed stakes called a palisade, showed no damage other than that done by the storms that sometimes beat the island.

White and his shipmates gaped at the deserted place. "They must have gone of their own accord," he said heavily. "There are no signs of a fight."

"Captain, why didn't they leave a message saying where they went?" a sailor asked.

John White strode around the silent encampment. "What's this?" He pointed to the trunk of a tree. Rudely carved letters spelled out *Crotoan.* *

"Here's 'nother," someone called.

The second tree trunk bore the strange inscription C R O. A cross had been carved next to it.

"What's it mean?"

White shook his head. "I don't know." He cast a weather-wise gaze at the sky. "The stormy season's coming on. We have to get away from here before a hurricane strikes." They searched the area a little more

---

*Later spelled *Croatan*, meaning either an Indian tribe or place.

A LAST MESSAGE FROM THE LOST COLONY

but found nothing other than the mysterious carvings on the tree trunks. The colony that had vanished became known as the Lost Colony. Over the years speculation and legends about Virginia Dare and her people ran wild. Some said they were carried off by a tribe of Indians once known as the Croatans. Others said it wasn't so. In any event, a broken-hearted John White sailed away, never to know what had happened to his beloved family.

Sir Walter Raleigh sent no more expeditions to America. Twelve years later, James, King of Scotland, succeeded Elizabeth the Great to the throne of England. He believed Raleigh's enemies who said the former trusted Captain of the Queen's Guard was a traitor and threw him into prison. During the thirteen years before he was executed, Raleigh wrote a history of the world.

Many of the English people hated their new king. They believed it would be better to sail to America

JOHN WHITE NEVER KNEW WHAT HAPPENED ON ROANOKE.

and live among hostile Indians and wild beasts than to stay and be subject to the cruel rule of King James.

In those days, people in Europe believed that common people received only the rights given by the king, but the king got his rights from God. King James said that one of those rights was owning America. Businessmen formed groups. Sir Robert Cecil found men willing to live in Virginia, take the land from the Indians, and give them Christianity in return! "After all," Cecil reasoned, "this offers the naked savages a chance to go to heaven when they die."

Cecil mustered a body of daring men and a seasoned sea captain named Christopher Newport and sent them to America. They crossed the Atlantic, fighting wind and wave. Long months later, after an exhausting search for a good place to build a colony, they sailed between two jutting capes and up a huge bay. Six mighty rivers entered it. The colonists-to-be chose the one farthest south and named it for their

CECIL MUSTERED A BODY OF DARING MEN.

king. Thirty-two miles from its mouth, they landed on a peninsula in April, 1607, and built a palisade and the rough houses that founded Jamestown.

"Have you ever seen such a land?" some gloated. "It's nothing like England! Just look at those forests, the mighty rivers."

"Too bad so many of us who set sail aboard the *Susan Constant*, the *Godspeed,* and the *Discovery* didn't live to see it," one said somberly.

The others fell silent, remembering the burial at sea of one-third of their number. Virginia continued to amaze them, with its oppressive summer heat, ear-splitting thunderstorms, and distances a mind could scarcely imagine. The settlers scorned the Indians' nakedness and sweltered in their English clothing and heavy shoes or tall boots. Pilgrims from a far country, they understood neither the land, its people, nor its possibilities.

All this lowered the spirits of men used to living

THEY UNDERSTOOD NEITHER THE LAND NOR ITS PEOPLE.

among many people. Now, outside of their own greatly reduced band and the Indians who glided through the forest or down the river in dugout canoes, they were alone in the wilderness. Captain Newport had gone back for other colonists. Would he get to England? If he did, could he get back? They desperately needed more people and supplies. As each passing month brought them closer to the expected time of Newport's return, they set a man to keep watch at the river's mouth.

At last he spotted the sails. "They've come! They've come!" he shouted, running into their midst like a man possessed.

"Thank God!" they cried. "We will call the watchman's spot Newport News."

Chief among their problems was their unfamiliarity with the country and its inhabitants, human and otherwise.

"How does a bloke know what he can eat?" the

"THEY'VE COME! THEY'VE COME, THANK GOD!"

colonists complained when food supplies ran low. "And the snakes. Who'd a-thought a snake gentleman enough to rattle would turn around and bite the bejabbers outa you?" A few settlers died from snakebite before the colonists learned about rattlesnakes. Others barely escaped with their lives.

"Stop yer bellyachin', mate," someone ordered. "At least the Indians ain't bothered us."

"Not yet," another significantly added. "I seen 'em staring at us, though."

"They're just curious," came the retort, but faces lengthened. Many a settler heartily wished himself back across the Atlantic.

A year later, two-thirds of the Jamestown colonists were dead. Wild and reckless, they had sailed under orders to find gold, discover a shortcut to the other ocean,* convert the heathen Indians, and provide goods to make England rich. Instead of clearing and planting, they searched for gold. A good joke on them

---

*The Pacific Ocean.

TWO-THIRDS OF THE JAMESTOWN COLONISTS WERE DEAD.

was mistaking iron pyrite—fool's gold—for the real thing and loading it into Newport's ships bound for England!

One of the seven council members to manage the Jamestown colony was the famous Captain John Smith. Temporarily banned from the council meetings for fighting, he promptly got himself a small boat and began to explore the country. Smith loved to boast. No one knew if half his tales were true, but he possessed a strong body and little fear. Both served him well, especially when he became governor and began to deal with the Indians—including Powhatan and Pocahontas.

CAPTAIN JOHN SMITH, FEARLESS AND STRONG

"STRANGERS ARE IN OUR LAND!"

3

Two Tribes Meet

"Pocahontas, Pocahontas!" Matachanna raced toward her sister, black braids flying like two frightened crows. "Have you heard?"

Pocahontas cocked her shining head to one side and looked up from the clothing she was washing in the stream near their home. "Heard?"

"Strangers are in our land. Even now they walk in the forests."

Pocahontas laughed. "Strangers are always in our forest," she reminded. "Is not our father the great Powhatan, chief of many tribes? Do chiefs not come to him for counsel?"

The black braids flew again when the other girl shook her head vigorously. "It is not Indian chiefs who come!" Her forehead wrinkled. "I have heard of tribes with light skins, but the strangers' faces are pale as morning frost. The men are bundled up like papooses, although the day is warm." She giggled. "Their feet go *clomp clomp* from the high and heavy coverings on their feet." Matachanna lifted her bare feet one at a time and clomped in front of her sister the way the white men walked.

A broad smile crossed Pocahontas's face. "Come help me. I too must see the strangers."

The girls quickly finished beating the clothing clean, hung the garments over nearby bushes to dry in the sun, and ran lightly down the trail into the nearby forest. When they heard voices, they lightly sprang behind a clump of bushes and lay on the ground. Pocahontas put her fingers over her mouth in warning so Matachanna would keep silent. A memory from long ago teased at her mind. She tried hard to remember.

"THEIR FEET GO CLOMP CLOMP."

When she did, a trickle of fear ran down her spine. Once before white-skinned men had come to her father's kingdom. The night wind had mournfully whispered the news that a chief lay dead in the forest. The son of a chief had been taken by the bearded strangers. Powhatan turned black in the face with anger. Yet fall, winter, spring, and summer had come and gone three times. With each passing year, the belief had grown that the spirits had driven the strangers away.

Now Pocahontas wondered. Why had they come again? She lay prone, daring to raise her head only enough to see into the small clearing.

Matachanna shifted position beside her. The carpet of pine needles beneath her rustled. Pocahontas drew her dark eyebrows together in a frown. *What might the strangers do if they found two girls spying on them?* She clutched her sister's arm and lay perfectly still. Perhaps they could hear something important.

SHE REMEMBERED THE DEAD CHIEF AND HIS SON.

Disappointment swept through her when she caught the sound of harsh-sounding words spoken in a language she did not understand. Loud laughter such as came from the braves of her tribe when they staged mock battles sent a shiver through her. One man stood out from among the score who swarmed around the clearing. Not from beauty, for he had little. Yet his strong body, the way he threw his head back and waved his arms to the others, showed he must be their chief.

Pocahontas observed every man there worked at some task. A long time later she learned that after John Smith had been named Governor, some of the settlers thought of themselves too highly. They clung to the idea that gentlemen should not work clearing and planting. Governor Smith knew everyone must work and help raise food or the whole community would starve. He set his mouth in a thin line and barked, "He that will not work, neither shall he eat."

The fine gentlemen knew he meant what he said.

HE MUST BE THEIR CHIEF!

They threw aside their lofty airs and pitched in alongside the commonest of those in Jamestown. Sickness and old age were the only reasons for not working recognized by Governor Smith's law.

Pocahontas squeezed Matachanna's arm and silently formed the word *come* with her lips. Inch by inch they slid away, until they put enough distance between them and the white men to make it safe to rise and run toward home. When they arrived, the girls sought out Powhatan and told him what they'd seen.

A scowl grew on his face, and he grunted. If he feared the changes the coming of the white men might bring, he hid it from his daughters. Yet when they teased to know about the pale-faced strangers, he told them some tribes near Jamestown were friendly to the pale faces and had already begun to trade with them.

"Others are not," he said in his deep voice. "There are those who lie in wait, bows and arrows ready, outside the English fort."

IF HE FEARED THE WHITE MEN, HE HID IT WELL.

"What is an English fort?" Matachanna wanted to know, eyes round.

"My brother, Opechancanough, says the bearded men come in giant dugouts with sheets flapping above them, from a land called England, far across the great waters. A fort is the log wall they build around their houses." He snorted. "If the coat-wearing people were not so foolish, they would know to cut down the tall grass outside their fort. That way, Indians could not hide in it, waiting for them to come out."

"Perhaps you could tell them, Father," Matachanna suggested.

An odd expression crept over Powhatan's face. "Perhaps I could. I have been thinking about trading with the white skins." His eyes gleamed brightly. "It is said they have shooting sticks that make noise like thunder." He clapped his hands over his ears. "When they speak, a deer falls in the forest. I would like to have a stick that shoots thunder instead of arrows."

INDIANS COULD HIDE IN THE TALL GRASS BY THE FORT.

"What would you trade?" Pocahontas asked, marveling at a tribe that had thunder in a stick.

"They want maize." Puzzlement came to Powhatan's face. "Do they not have it in their country? My chiefs tell me these English in their fort cannot seem to get enough maize. We have much." He waved his bare, brown arm toward the fields of cornstalks growing tall and green around the village.

"Soon the corn will ripen," Pocahontas said. Her heart beat with excitement. "It will be the celebration of the harvest." She thought of the games and races, the singing and feasting. Great fires would send their smoke to the skies. Men, women, and children would circle around them, giving thanks for the bountiful harvest.

"Do the English trade only shooting sticks?" Matachanna asked.

Powhatan shook his head and grinned. "I have heard that sometimes they give a kettle of copper. Or a

"DO THE ENGLISH TRADE ONLY SHOOTING STICKS?"

sword." He fondly looked at his daughters. "The white skins have wampum not made of shells like ours and ones with tongues that sing like birds."*

"Father, when the harvest celebration is ended, will you go? May we go with you?" Pocahontas begged.

Powhatan folded his arms across his wide chest. "I will think."

All through the happy time of celebration, Pocahontas and Matachanna hoped and dreamed of perhaps going with their father to see the English fort. They learned it was called Jamestown, after the English king. "Just as Powhatan is called for our mighty father," they agreed. Curiosity grew until they could barely wait for the long-anticipated harvest feast to end!

At last Powhatan decided to take advantage of the big corn crop and see if he could get a stick that shot thunder. He and many others from the village banded together to go to Jamestown. He agreed to let

---

*Glass beads and small bells.

MANY FROM THE VILLAGE WENT TO JAMESTOWN.

Pocahontas go with him, but not Matachanna. "One must stay with her mother," he ordered.

Matachanna's eyes filled with tears.

"Don't cry, my sister. I will bring you the new wampum," Pocahontas whispered. "I will tell you everything I see when I return." Matachanna dried her tears and waved good-bye, still looking disappointed.

"We will take much," Powhatan decided. "Surely the English chief will want what we bring." Heavily laden, they slowly made their way to Jamestown.

When they reached the fort, they laid down their burdens of corn, berries and nuts, pumpkins, squash, and turkeys. The half-starved settlers devoured the food like wolves do their prey. Powhatan watched them, arms folded in his usual position. Some of the settlers had learned the Powhatan language. They spoke to the chief now known as Master of Tidewater Virginia. "We thank you. To show our thanks, we give you these." They placed some copper, beads, bells,

THE HALF-STARVED SETTLERS DEVOURED THE FOOD.

and hatchets before Powhatan.

Powhatan made known his wish to have a shooting stick. Even before the coat-wearing chief spoke, the Indian chief knew he would get none. John Smith had given an order that no Indian would be given guns or even allowed to handle them.

Pocahontas hung back a goodly distance, as befitted an Indian maiden. Pah, what cared she for sticks that shot thunder? Her fascinated gaze remained fixed on the shining wampum before her father, the merry bells that did indeed sing like birds. Every maiden in their village would envy her and Matachanna. She proudly raised her head. The daughters of Powhatan deserved respect and honor.

Powhatan motioned for his braves to collect the bounty for which they'd traded food. He started away on silent feet and smiled at Pocahontas. His mouth twitched with amusement. Then he turned back and called, so clearly she could hear from her distant po-

THE DAUGHTERS OF POWHATAN DESERVED HONOR.

sition, "If you would be safe from your enemies, Powhatan says cut down the long grass." He gestured to the tall, waving grass outside the fort. "Snakes waiting to strike will have no place to hide." He strode away, shoulders straight.

Pocahontas ducked her head and giggled. Some of the white men looked her way. She felt hot blood rise to her cheeks, then quickly disappeared into the forest.

"SNAKES WILL HAVE NO PLACE TO HIDE."

FRIENDLY RELATIONS CONTINUED WITH THE COLONISTS.

4

Pocahontas, Brave Maiden

During the first three years after the establishment of the Jamestown colony, the settlers died by the fifties and hundreds. Powhatan and his warriors could easily have wiped them out at any time or let them weaken and die from starvation. Instead, he sent help. Governor John Smith and his people never expected the kindness shown to them in the black days that came to Jamestown like a thundercloud of doom.

Friendly relations continued between Powhatan and the colonists; both parties were shrewd enough to see their advantages. The London joint-stock company that owned and operated Jamestown, though, had greedy eyes turned toward making all the profit the New World afforded.

Powhatan wisely decided he'd rather trade with the English than make war with them. He told Captain John Smith, "It is foolish of you to try and take what you want by force. It is better to get those things through friendship. Would you destroy the ones who brought food when you would have starved without it?

"Powhatan is wise, like the fox in the forest. He knows it is better to eat good meat, be well, and sleep quietly with his women and children than to fight. Powhatan says, laugh and be merry with the English. Be their friend, not their enemy. Then Powhatan have what he wants: copper, hatchets, and many other things."

Although John Smith agreed, Powhatan and his people were not treated fairly. They did not know how to trade, and so received trifles for their bushels of corn. Still, they taught the settlers how to grow maize,

"IT IS BETTER TO GET THINGS THROUGH FRIENDSHIP."

potatoes, squash, and pumpkins. They showed them good places to catch fish from the streams and animals from the woods.*

John Smith, who was young and strong, liked nothing better than exploring every inlet, every stream. Everywhere he went, he made maps. He drew rivers no one else had ever drawn, and he named them with English names. The wild country satisfied something deep inside him, a love for adventure and appreciation for living in this place at this time.

One wintry day, Smith took an Indian guide and walked inland from the rest of his small exploring party who remained by the river. From out of nowhere, arrows sang through the air without warning, seeming

---

*Later, colonists had plenty of corn, but the Indians had none. Instead of treating the Indians as they had treated the settlers, the English used the power of food to their own advantage. They forced the desperate Indians to sign away valuable land in order to keep from starving.

THE WILD COUNTRY SATISFIED SOMETHING DEEP INSIDE HIM.

to come from every direction!

Using his quick wits, Smith grabbed his guide and held him as a shield with one hand, firing his pistol with the other. Two of the more than a hundred Indians fell. The others screeched with hatred.

"Do not kill him," the terrified guide yelled. His eyes rolled in fear for his own life. "He is a chief."

The Indians hesitated, then jabbered together. John's hopes rose. Killing a chief was not a thing the tribes did lightly; they preferred more ceremony.

The Indians continued arguing, then reluctantly agreed to lay aside their bows if Smith would put down his gun.

"No!" John gripped his guide even more tightly. He backed away, still holding his pistol and thinking, *If I reach the river I will have help.* He didn't know that two of the ten men who had started on the expedition with him lay dead on the banks of the river he

SMITH USED HIS GUIDE AS A SHIELD.

had just left—or that the others had fled from the Indian attack.

Before he reached the river, he and the guide fell into a swamp. There was no way for John to get out and still hold onto the Indian and his pistol!

At last, he threw it aside. His heart pounded. Every story of white persons captured by the Indians rose to taunt him. He stared into the unfriendly faces and considered. Outnumbered by more than a hundred to one and weaponless, he had no chance of fighting his way free. Neither could he make a break into the forest. The Indians knew it far better than he did.

"Take me to Powhatan," he demanded in a loud and clear voice. A ripple of respect ran through the circle of warriors that the white man showed no fear.

During the next weeks, his captors paraded him from village to village. So far, he had not been tortured. Instead, the chiefs asked questions, wanting to

"TAKE ME TO POWHATAN," HE DEMANDED.

know why the white skins had come to their land.

At last, he did reach Powhatan. Relying on boldness as the only way perhaps to save his life, Smith went into a rage. "Why am I being treated like this?" he demanded.

Pocahontas and Matachanna peeped from behind their home, eyes wide at the sight of the short, straight man with fearless eyes and a beard like a wolf's pelt. Powhatan, an Indian chief who sometimes allowed his moods to rule him instead of his usual common sense, rose to full height. "Bind him," he ordered.

His braves sprang to obey. John Smith soon sat securely tied to a large tree. Powhatan fired off a hundred questions. Was Smith a spy, determined to learn Powhatan's weaknesses so he could attack the village and take his women and children? If not, why did the coat-wearer look at Powhatan's rivers and streams and make marks on a paper?

"WHY AM I BEING TREATED LIKE THIS?"

John answered as best he could. His queen in England desired to know more of Virginia, its forests and waterways.

Powhatan remained unsatisfied. "I will decide."

The captive went hot, then cold. Occasionally, a tribe adopted a white man into the tribe. Should he plead for his life, promise many gifts if he were spared? Nay. Doing so would show weakness. His only hope lay in continuing boldly. Indians admired courage.

Pocahontas had seen what Powhatan had done to the enemies he had captured. Now she wondered. Why had her father turned against the white man? She longed to ask but held back. A chieftain's daughter had no right to question her father.

For several days, John Smith stayed in the Indian village, always under close guard, always hoping for a moment's carelessness on someone's part. If only he could free himself from the thongs that held him,

HE STAYED IN THE INDIAN VILLAGE UNDER CLOSE GUARD.

perhaps in the dead of night he could steal away while his captors lay sleeping. He wondered why no one from the colony came to rescue him but soon gave up the notion. How could a handful of men who could barely keep life in their bodies form a rescue party against an Indian nation that numbered in the thousands?

Another thought tormented him. The colonists had come to America to bring salvation to the Indians. It seemed strange that God first allowed those who came in His name to nearly starve, then permitted their leader to be executed by the very persons the English had come to save! Say, was that not what had happened to Jesus? Those He had come to save had turned on Him, had taken His life.

John Smith muttered to himself, "It's not the same. Jesus rose from the dead and left the plan of salvation. All I'll leave behind are my maps." He bowed

JOHN SMITH REBELLED AGAINST DEATH.

his head, rebelling that he must die while still young. How much he must leave undone! Powhatan's delay in making a decision showed how small any hope of being freed really was. John shuddered. There seemed nothing left to do but pray that death would come swiftly.

He threw aside the blanket of fear that threatened to make of him a sniveling coward. Never! If he must die, it would be as an Englishman and a gentleman. Forcing his heated blood to coolness, he began to plan. The most likely form of execution was burning at the stake. The Indians would loosen the bonds that held him to the tree, jerk their captive to his feet and securely tie him to a wooden post. His only hope of freedom lay in the brief moments when they untied him from the tree.

Would his strong legs, numbed from their long exposure to the ground, serve him? If so, he would spring

HE WOULD DIE AS AN ENGLISHMAN AND A GENTLEMAN.

up and dart away. Better to receive a hail of arrows than to be burned alive.

John Smith's plans came to naught. The very next day Powhatan came toward him, stone war club held high. There would be no brief moment, no chance to make a final fight. A single blow of the club held in Powhatan's strong hands and—eternity. John silently offered a last prayer. Only a miracle could save him now.

The miracle came on flying, moccasin-clad feet. Pocahontas, braids flying as they did when she outran a storm, hurled herself between Powhatan and John Smith. She fell to her knees, placed her head on the captive's, and pleaded, "No, Father, you must not kill him!"

She heard Matachanna's gasp and her mother's dismayed grunt. Powhatan stared at her with bottomless, black eyes. No longer the playful papoose or the berry-

"NO, FATHER, YOU MUST NOT KILL HIM!"

stained little girl, Pocahontas's face held a woman's determination.

"Get up," her father ordered.

For the first time in her life, she did not obey. "I cannot, Father, until you say you will spare him."

For one terrible moment, she thought he would kill her as well as John Smith. So be it. Something inside would not allow her to submit to his will. She saw anger rise then dwindle in her father's eyes. She saw his struggle between his love for her and the need to change his order.

Love won.

Powhatan laid down his war club, whipped out a sharp knife, and cut the doomed man's bonds.

POWHATAN LAID DOWN HIS WAR CLUB. . . .

THE ANGRY CAPTAIN NEWPORT

5
Another Father

At last, Captain Newport returned, smarting from the reception he had received in England. The backers of the Jamestown colony had been furious when the rocks stored in the hold of Newport's ship had been discovered to be worthless. "Where is the gold we sent you for?" they had demanded. "Did we not pay good money to outfit the expedition? We sent you to bring us riches and you bring us rocks!" Deep frowns had turned their faces ugly. "When you come again, bring real gold or you will answer to us!"

Newport's anger grew when he reached the settlement with the much-needed food supplies. Where were the crops the settlers should have raised by now? He surveyed the thirty-eight, all that were left of those who had crossed with him earlier. "Have you done nothing but fight among yourselves?"

They hastened to explain how they had nearly starved. Newport sighed. "Fill your bellies with good English beef and pork," he told them. "Then get busy."

Alas for good intentions, for just a few days later, fire raced through the village. Thatched roofs, buildings, the church, and even the storehouse with most of the precious food from England fell before the hungry flames.

Powhatan proved himself a true friend in the colonists' time of distress. At least once a week he sent food-bearers. Pocahontas accompanied them, glorying in the chance to see and learn more of the white men and their ways. During this time, she lived in two worlds—her Indian village and Jamestown.

Powhatan and the English had exchanged young men to learn the language and serve as interpreters. An Indian maiden could not do such a thing, but

FIRE RACED THROUGH THE SETTLEMENT.

Pocahontas had ears made keen to every rustle in the forest. She used them to learn the white man's language. The few boys in the settlement heralded her visits with whoops of joy, admiring her ability to leap and run in games and races. The English boys taught her acrobatics. She soon did handsprings and turned cartwheels with the best of them!

As much as she enjoyed such sport, Pocahontas liked best to talk with John Smith. He deeply appreciated her bringing corn and other food and called her blessed in his journal. He believed God used the Indian maiden as "an instrument to preserve. . .the colony from death, famine, and utter confusion."

Matachanna eagerly awaited her sister's return from her visits to the settlement, for Pocahontas brought back many gifts from John Smith. Yet Captain Newport and Smith differed greatly in their feelings toward the Indians. Newport believed the Indians were friendly and allowed his men to trade freely. Smith

SMITH BELIEVED GOD USED POCAHONTAS AS
"AN INSTRUMENT TO PRESERVE THE COLONY...."

felt the natives must be ruled with an iron hand. He also feared what would happen once Newport sailed again. His men had spoiled the Indians by giving them what they asked for, even swords—something Smith had never allowed. It made the Indians bold. When they couldn't get swords and hatchets by trading, they stole them.

Newport sailed again, taking one of Powhatan's servants, a young man learning English. Powhatan was eager to learn what the faraway country of England was like. Namontack would report everything he saw.

Meanwhile, the few remaining colonists began to work together as a community. No more did fine gentlemen keep their hands soft and white while the commoners tilled the land. John Smith's order that only those who worked would be given food took root and grew. Men carried guns when they went to work in the fields. In America there were no armies to protect the people. All had to work and fight together.

THE INDIANS STOLE SWORDS AND HATCHETS.

One of the most curious things Pocahontas learned from John Smith, Reverend Hunt, and others who talked with her was that the palefaces believed in only one God. She found it hard to understand. "Do you not worship spirits of the animals?" Pocahontas shivered. "Are you not afraid of the creator, the Great Hare?"

"The God we serve is mightier than all the animals, for He made them," Reverend Hunt explained. "Pocahontas, many seasons ago, long before Powhatan's great-great-ever-so-many-great ancestors lived, God made the world and everything in it. He created the trees and flowers. He made the grass and the sun and stars and sky, the thunder and lightning, the wind and rain. He even made the Great Hare you pray to and fear."

"How could He do this?" Her breath came fast and her dark gaze never left her teacher's face.

"He is more powerful than anything on earth or in

"THE GOD WE SERVE IS MIGHTIER THAN ALL THE ANIMALS."

the heavens. God made a man from the dust of the earth and breathed life into him. Then he made a companion for the man—a woman, formed from a rib taken from the man while he lay in a deep sleep."

Pocahontas's eyes glistened. She eagerly waited to hear more.

"God put the man and the woman, who were called Adam and Eve, into a beautiful garden where everything was peaceful. They had nothing to fear. Sin and death had not entered the world. No animal hunted another, but dwelt together in peace. God gave Adam and Eve only one rule. They could gather and eat fruit from every tree in the beautiful garden except one. If they disobeyed Him and ate from the tree called the knowledge of good and evil, they would die. For a time all went well. Then the devil, called Satan or the serpent, told Eve a terrible lie. He said they would not die at all and that God didn't want them to eat from that tree for fear they would become gods, too!"

"WHAT DID THE MAIDEN EVE DO?"

"What did the maiden Eve do?" Pocahontas could hardly wait to hear more.

"She ate fruit from the tree and gave some to Adam, who also ate."

"Did God send thunder and lightning to punish them?"

"No, but He drove them from the garden and put an angel with a flaming sword at the entrance. They could never go back inside again."

Pocahontas didn't know about flaming swords, but she knew her father and other chiefs sometimes tipped their arrows with flame and shot them to set enemy camps on fire. "Why did they not obey God?" she cried.

Reverend Hunt looked old and tired. "They listened to the Evil One instead of to God," he slowly said. His eyes gradually brightened. "The story didn't end there, praise to His name! Adam and Eve worked hard to till the ground. They had children and grandchil-

INDIANS SOMETIMES TIPPED THEIR ARROWS WITH FLAME.

dren, and the earth became filled with people.

"Pocahontas, you know how much your father loves you?"

"Oh, yes."

"We all have another Father, child. God is the Father of us all. He loves us even more than Powhatan loves you!"

Pocahontas's eyes grew round with surprise. "That cannot be. My father would die before allowing anything to harm me!"

"God loved you and me and all the people who ever lived or ever will live," Reverend Hunt told her. "He loves us so much He sent His only Son to die and take all our sins on Him so someday we can live with Him in a place of peace and happiness. There will never again be war between Indian tribes or between white-and brown-skinned people."

"How do you know these things?"

"God Himself has spoken and told us, child."

"MY FATHER WOULD DIE BEFORE ALLOWING
ANYTHING TO HARM ME!"

A memory from long ago came to mind. Pocahontas closed her eyes. She saw herself as a small girl, close to her mother who sat weaving a basket. Clear as the waterfall she loved came their long-ago conversation. *Mother, wouldn't it be wonderful if when we pray, the Great Hare and animal spirits we pray to would reply? Is it not rude to give no answer when someone speaks to you?*

Pocahontas opened her eyes. She gazed into the reverend's face, searching for the truth. Her heart pounded like many war drums. "Your God who is another Father answers when you speak to Him? How?"

"In many ways, Pocahontas. Sometimes it is a tiny voice deep in one's soul that warns us to do right." Reverend Hunt picked up a worn, black book from the table. "This is another way God speaks to His children."

Pocahontas curiously fingered the strange markings

"THIS IS ANOTHER WAY GOD SPEAKS TO HIS CHILDREN."

on the cover. "What does it say?"

"Holy Bible. It is a record of God's dealings with His people from the time of Adam and Eve until after God sent His Son to save us." The minister quickly sketched in the birth of Christ in the manger at Bethlehem and how nothing in the world had been the same since He had come.

The Indian girl opened the book. "If only I could know what it says!" She touched the rows of black figures marching like soldiers across the pages.

"You can, Pocahontas, if you are willing to work hard," he promised.

Many things came to pass before that happened. A band of roving Indians set upon John Smith. Somehow, he managed to escape—and arrived back in Jamestown, along with the seven Indians he had taken captive.

Powhatan attempted to get them released. John Smith would not let them go. At last, Powhatan sent

"IF ONLY I COULD KNOW WHAT IT SAYS!"

Pocahontas with a small party and a fine deer. "Do not beg," he told her. "You are the daughter of a king. Rawhunt and the others may beg. You are simply to remind Captain Smith of your father's friendship."

Princess Pocahontas did as ordered. Smith released his prisoners, then sailed off on more explorations. Pocahontas grew tall and thought much about the white man's God who had sent His Son to die and save all the tribes of the world.

POCAHONTAS GREW TALL AND THOUGHT MUCH ABOUT GOD.

AN ENCOUNTER WITH A STINGRAY THREATENED SMITH'S LIFE.

6

King Powhatan

John Smith's Virginia expeditions left him speech-less. He found fur-bearing animals whose skins would bring a fortune in England. Fish crowded the rivers and streams. An encounter with a stingray threatened his life but by no means lessened his thirst for exploring.

The arrival of Captain Newport with seventy new settlers, two of them women, drastically changed things. He had brought no supplies, just bizarre orders from the London company:

1. Seek more diligently for gold.

2. Manufacture glass and make pitch and tar. (Eight Dutchmen and Poles had been sent to show the settlers how.)

3. Crown Powhatan so he will be a ruler under King James!

They sent gifts for Powhatan, among them a bed so enormous it could only be transported by barge up the river—an eighty-mile trip, when Werowocomoco lay just twelve miles from Jamestown! A copper crown had been provided for the coronation.

John Smith took Namontack, who had returned from England filled with wonder, and a few Jamestown men to tell Powhatan of the great honor being bestowed by the English king. Powhatan wasn't home, but Pocahontas offered a warm welcome.

Little trace of the friendly chief who had cared for the starving colonists showed in Powhatan's face when he arrived and acknowleged the messengers. White men walked his land. They carried guns and wanted corn but treated Powhatan rudely.

"I shall not come to you," he growled. "I *am* a king. Let the presents from your king be brought to me. I

*"I SHALL NOT COME TO YOU, FOR I **AM** A KING!"*

have heard much from Namontack of your England."
His dark eyes showed contempt for a race who built
great buildings and bridges, yet let their people starve.

Over a hundred Englishmen gathered for the crowning of King Powhatan. Resplendent in a red coat,
Powhatan absolutely refused to kneel. Why should he,
who was already a king, bend his knees to the white
skins? Even the feel of the copper crown once put on
his head didn't lessen his resentment.

The English left. Powhatan gave an order to his
people. "No more will we trade with the whites," he
said. "My daughter, you will go to Jamestown no more.
John Smith and his people are our enemies now. They
call us friends and steal our land." He folded his arms
across his broad chest. "King Powhatan has spoken.
Let all hear and obey."

Pocahontas felt sick. She had grown fond of John
Smith in the time she had talked with him. She couldn't
believe he was their enemy. Yet she could not protest.

RESPLENDENT IN RED COAT, POWHATAN REFUSED TO KNEEL.

Her father's orders must be obeyed, no matter how she felt.

Pocahontas had no way of knowing how cruel Smith could be when crossed. He was determined to make the colony a success, even if it meant war. His people could not be allowed to starve simply because Powhatan wanted swords and guns. John Smith shuddered to think what might happen once the Indians were armed with more than spears and bows and arrows.

After a time of silence, a summons came. Powhatan wanted Smith to visit and get a boatload of corn. He asked for all kinds of things in return, including a house built in the English style. John sent no guns or swords but did send four men to start building a house. He followed two weeks later, well guarded. His anger rose when he learned the carpenters liked living with Powhatan better than living in Jamestown. They refused to go back.

JOHN SMITH WAS VERY CRUEL WHEN CROSSED.

Powhatan and John Smith, once bound by friendship, quarreled violently.

Powhatan stalked out, then slipped away with his wives and children, including Pocahontas. He left braves to surround the house. John grew wary when he caught sight of the warriors. He fired his pistol, and the braves ran into the forest, babbling that Powhatan's plan to kill Smith had failed.

Pocahontas gasped. She must warn the man she still thought of as her friend. In the dead of night, she slipped through the forest on silent feet. She kept under cover until she saw Smith alone, then whispered a warning before fleeing back to her people. Even though Powhatan loved his favorite daughter, tribe loyalty meant he must order her killed if he discovered she had warned his enemies.

Opechancanough and others made attempts on Smith's life. All failed. Tales ran through the trees that the white man had powerful magic and could not

POCAHONTAS WHISPERED A WARNING BEFORE FLEEING.

be killed.

John reached Jamestown and found he was the only member of the council still alive, due to a boat accident. For a time, things again improved. Then—rats! Dozens of the grisly creatures came off the English ships. They bred and raised more rats that ate everything in sight, including the carefully hoarded corn saved for planting. The settlers had to live off the land, eating fish and oysters, searching to find any friendly Indians who might help them.

Three hundred new settlers arrived. So did the news that John Smith was being replaced by his old enemies. After three years of serving Virginia, he loved the New World and would never leave it permanently, but for now, he returned to London.

Little birds in the forest tittle-tattled the news. The wind picked it up. Pocahontas wondered, and the Indians rejoiced. With the magic man who could not die gone, what was to stop them from driving the En-

THE RATS ATE EVERYTHING IN SIGHT!

glish away forever?

Powhatan had gone from Werowocomoco. Past seventy, he knew the Jamestown colonists could not hold out much longer. Soon the whites would leave his kingdom. The old days would return, with the Powhatan Confederacy in control of the land.

So began a year known forever as the Starving Time. No colonist dared leave the fort for fear of being killed. Starvation and disease took their toll on the people who ate everything available—dogs, horses, mice, and even the filthy rats. A few deserted to whatever Indians would take them in. Some settlers lost their lives when approaching "friendly" Indians to get food.

One greening spring day, Powhatan said to Pocahontas, "My daughter, now that you have seen fourteen seasons, you have found favor in the eyes of Captain Kocoum."

Pocahontas modestly looked down, as befitted an Indian maiden.

"YOU HAVE FOUND FAVOR IN THE EYES OF CAPTAIN KOCOUM."

"Kocoum is eager to make you his squaw," Powhatan continued. "I have promised you to him."

She looked into her father's eyes. How kind they were when they gazed on her, yet how ugly when he spoke of the English! Pocahontas thought of Kocoum. She had not been unaware of how the warrior watched her since she had become a young woman. Son of a chief, many of the maidens admired him. Yet he had chosen her. Pocahontas felt her face warm with the rich, red blood that flowed in her veins. "If Kocoum pleases my father, I shall become his squaw."

An Indian princess in her own right, marriage with Kocoum gave Pocahontas added status and respect. Kocoum filled an empty part of her, but not completely. When she tried to talk with him about the God of the whites, he scowled fiercely and told her not to be a foolish woman. There were no gods other than those Powhatan worshiped. "If the whites had a powerful God, would He not have protected Jamestown?" he

"THERE ARE NO GODS BUT THOSE OF THE POWHATAN!"

reasoned.

Pocahontas did not reply, yet deep inside she continued to wonder and regret. If only she had learned to know what the tiny black soldiers marching across the pages of the book Reverend Hunt called the Holy Bible meant! She no longer felt satisfied with praying to the Great Hare, who never answered. She felt her prayers became lost before they reached the ceiling of her home.

Pocahontas hated war. Why couldn't there be the peace the minister said God wanted between white skins and Indians? When her husband Kocoum was killed she wondered even more. But months followed weeks and there was no peace.

By the spring of 1610, only one out of ten original colonists still lived. Those gallant half a hundred dully wondered why they had survived. All hope of relief had died when Captain Newport's ship was reported lost at sea.

POCAHONTAS MOURNED THE LOSS OF HER HUSBAND.

One beautiful May day, Newport returned. His flag-ship had not sunk but had been blown to one of the Bermuda islands and destroyed. Not one passenger had been lost. The island had plenty of fruit, wild hogs, fish, and birds. The 150 stranded travelers built huts with leaf-thatched roofs. They salvaged wood from the wrecked ships and built two large boats and crowded aboard. They could only take enough food for the two- to three-week journey, but what did it matter? Jamestown would be a thriving colony with plenty for all by now.

The scene that awaited them filled them with hor-ror. Most of the friends they'd known lay deep in the earth beneath rude crosses. The few gaunt persons who greeted them could barely stand.

Governor Gates rang the church bell and summoned all who could walk to a service. Only God could save them now; the new arrivals had food for themselves for only a few days and none for the settlers. "There is

THE SCENE THAT AWAITED THEM FILLED THEM WITH HORROR!

no use fighting the Indians," one survivor stated. "This is planting time, not harvest."

On June 7, Governor Gates said everyone must leave the colony. He ordered the cannon buried. Some wanted to set fire to the fort. Gates said no.

The boats started toward the coast and disappeared from the sight of watching Indian scouts. How they screeched! The white men had at last been driven away. The scouts could hardly wait to spread the news. Relief would cover the land like a blanket, and Powhatan would dance with gladness in spite of his many years.

THE WHITE MEN HAD AT LAST BEEN DRIVEN AWAY!

THEY RETURNED TO JAMESTOWN.

7

There Is No Peace

The Indian scouts who watched Governor Gates and the last of the white people leave Jamestown after an impressive musket salute, rejoiced too soon. At the very moment the disheartened, defeated band sailed away from Jamestown, other ships from London carrying new commanders, 150 new settlers, and food for a year were nearly there. They met on the river early the next morning. Now it was the colonists' turn to rejoice. They reversed directions and went back to Jamestown, a place most of the deserters had believed they would never see again.

How glad they were they had not burned the fort! Lord De La Warre, put in charge by England, set the people to work. Some went to distant tribes who were willing to trade, others on fishing and hunting expeditions. Gradually, Jamestown lived again. But Lord De La Warre made a bad choice by refusing to seek peace with Powhatan and the nearby Indians who threatened the whites. Terrible things happened on both sides. De La Warre demanded that Powhatan return stolen captives and weapons. Powhatan sneered and told the English to leave his kingdom and never come back.

De La Warre fell sick with malaria, followed by many other illnesses. Before a year passed, he gladly sailed back to London. His replacement was worse than De La Warre. Sir Thomas Dale believed the only way to govern was through harsh punishment when even the slightest rule was broken. The people lived in terror. Any man caught swearing three times paid with his life. Even picking flowers or fruit without permission meant dire punishment.

THOU SHALT **NOT** SWEAR, CUSS, OR, SPIT!

SIR THOMAS DALE BELIEVED IN HARSH PUNISHMENT.

Dale openly bragged, "Give me 2,000 English convicts, and I'll rid this country of Indians forever." He ordered attacks for no reason and gloried when the Indians' arrows could not pierce the metal armor his soldiers wore. Dale also built other forts and the fighting went on.

A new factor entered the colony and had a lasting effect on the whites, the Indians, and especially Pocahontas. One of the Englishmen who survived the Bermuda shipwreck was a young widower named John Rolfe. When he had first come to the colony, the Indians had taught him how to plant tobacco, one of the worst mistakes they ever made. They had no way of knowing it would contribute to the downfall of their way of life.

King James hated tobacco and branded it ugly, nasty, and bad for one's health. Still, smoking tobacco in pipes was highly fashionable among young English-

ARROWS COULD NOT PIERCE THE SOLDIERS' METAL ARMOR.

men. It started when (according to popular belief) Sir Walter Raleigh first brought tobacco to England in the late 1500s. Also according to gossip, a funny thing happened the first time a certain servant came in while Raleigh was lighting his pipe. Smoke poured from Sir Walter's mouth. The frightened servant thought he was on fire. He threw the tankard of ale he'd been carrying all over Sir Walter to "put out the fire."

The demand for tobacco (which wasn't grown in England) grew and grew. The type grown by the Indians in Virginia was a poor quality and unwanted. The young widower, John Rolfe, experimented with it. He learned to cut tobacco before it fully ripened, then cure it under shelter instead of in the sun. The first shipment he sent to England was hailed with delight. Rolfe and his fellow colonists began raising tobacco, a crop worth five to six times the profit of other crops. At one time, the streets of Jamestown were even used

THE DEMAND FOR TOBACCO GREW AND GREW.

for growing tobacco plants!

John Rolfe had been a gentleman in England. He had probably never set out to become a tobacco planter. He found, however, that America was sadly lacking in laborers to work a large estate, even though land could be easily obtained. Rolfe could not make a living by depending on others to do his work. So he decided to cultivate and improve tobacco until its quality matched the best to be had. It brought him a fortune.

Tobacco did more than bring in money and make people sick; tobacco even killed some people by putting poisonous smoke into the lungs of those ignorant of its effects. It increased greed to a fever pitch. The English, who had holdings in the New World, cared far more about their profits than anything else. Their attitude was, "If we have bigger profits through peace, well and good. If war brings us more money, then let

TOBACCO BROUGHT IN A FORTUNE!

us have war."

With the increasing market for tobacco, the colonists needed more and more land. Tobacco is hard on the land and requires that every two or three years, new land be used or the crops won't be profitable.

The early hard-working settlers cleared perhaps forty acres through mighty efforts. Later they got their hands on hundreds of acres by seizing an Indian village. Unscrupulous men reasoned, "Only a fool breaks his back clearing when all this land is here for the taking. Let the Indians clear the land. It is all they are good for, anyway. Once the fields are tilled and workable, we'll simply drive the villagers away and have the greater part of the work done for us."

The tribes valued their homes but were not willing to die for them. Again and again they moved, squaws, children, and maidens weeping, the braves and old men stone-faced and angry. As they migrated, they

"WE'LL SIMPLY DRIVE THE INDIANS AWAY!"

assured themselves, "Soon the white skins will have enough land." They could not understand the greed that drove those who believed themselves divinely appointed by God to rule the savages in this raw land. Over a period of four years, shipments of dried, cured tobacco leaves sent from Virginia to England rose from four barrels to over 50,000 pounds! It cost the Indians dearly.

The spring of 1613 found approximately 700 settlers in Virginia. Thirty or more of them were brave women. Some Indian tribes had made peace with the whites. Not Powhatan. He held aloof, remembering how his good will in helping the settlers had not kept them from taking his lands. By now he knew how worthless the trifles the English offered in exchange for land really were. Even though deep in his heart he longed for peace, he sometimes despaired.

"There is no peace," he declared, arms crossed in

"THERE IS NO PEACE," POWHATAN DECLARED.

the old way although his body had begun to show the signs of age sneaking up on him.

Some distance away in the home of the Potomac chief, seventeen-year-old Pocahontas had begun to believe her father was right. Since the loss of Kocoum, her heart had been sad, like the little bird whose mate falls to the ground and dies. Years had passed since she had talked with John Smith and Reverend Hunt. She could speak the English language well but had no Holy Bible. Even if she'd had the book the minister said held God's message to His children, she would not be able to read it.

In April of 1613, Samuel Argall, captain of the flagship *De La Warre,* came from Jamestown on a trading mission to the Potomac. To his delight, he learned Pocahontas was in the area.

"What an opportunity!" he told himself. "I will get the girl and hold her hostage. No harm need come to

SINCE THE LOSS OF KOCOUM, HER HEART HAD BEEN SAD.

her, but we shall have Powhatan right where we want him." He closed his hand and squeezed it. Indians and whites alike knew of the love the Algonquian chief had for his daughter. Once Powhatan knew Pocahontas had been captured, he'd have to return the stolen weapons and the captives the settlers had been trying to get back for such a long time. Powhatan would also be willing to make peace.

Argall knew better than to try an actual kidnapping in order to get her aboard his ship. Such a thing would cause an outcry that might result in a massive Indian uprising. He thought and thought. A fox-like smile crept over his face. The Potomac chief's brother was an old trading friend. Argall sought him out, showed him a beautiful copper kettle, and promised, "Help me get Pocahontas on my ship and it shall be yours."

The Indian and his squaw looked at the fine kettle with greedy eyes. The very next day they sought

THEY PLOTTED TO KIDNAP POCAHONTAS!

Pocahontas out and said they were going to go see an English ship anchored in the river. Perhaps she would also enjoy seeing it.

Once at the harbor, the squaw clapped her hands and demanded that her husband take her on board. He agreed, but only if Pocahontas accompanied them. She hesitated.

"I beg you, come," the woman pleaded. The tears in her eyes were real, not from disappointment over being unable to go aboard the English ship but because she feared the loss of the wonderful kettle!

Pocahontas at last gave in. Nothing warned her she was walking into a well-laid trap. Samuel Argall insisted the trio eat with him at the captain's table. After the meal, the Indian and his squaw secretly collected their prize kettle. Pocahontas did not suspect a plot against her until she tried to go ashore and the English surrounded her. "What is the meaning of this?

"WHAT IS THE MEANING OF THIS? LET ME PASS!"

Let me past!" she cried.

"You are going to Jamestown with us," she was told.

Pocahontas darted one way then another, seeking to break through the circle of men. She raved and argued. The Potomac Indian and his squaw pretended to be as outraged as she—for a little while. Then they went ashore, lugging their precious copper kettle with them and leaving Pocahontas to the mercy of Captain Argall and his crew.

SHE WAS AT THE MERCY OF CAPTAIN ARGALL AND HIS CREW!

THEY WATCHED POCAHONTAS WITH EAGLE EYES.

8

Captive Princess

Pocahontas was closely guarded on the trip to Jamestown. Captain Argall and his crew treated her respectfully but never left her alone. Even at night they guarded the entrance to her small sleeping space. She watched her captors through half-shut eyes. If she could get past them at a point where the river narrowed, she would throw herself into the water and swim to shore. Trained to swim long distances underwater, she might be able to reach the sheltering forest before they could launch a small boat and come after her. Once there, no white man on earth could keep up with her.

She sighed. The alert captain and his eagle-eyed crew did not permit her to even get close to the rail.

"No one will hurt you," Argall told her. "Any man who touches or frightens you will feel the keen edge of my blade." He pulled a knife from his belt. Its blade gleamed in the sun.

For a wild moment Pocahontas considered snatching it from him. Once armed, she could threaten to kill the captain unless he released her. Or put the point of the blade to her own heart. The captain probably considered her a stupid squaw. He couldn't know Pocahontas, captive princess, loved life far too much to kill herself. Argall would not dare take that chance.

She crouched, ready to spring. The slight movement brought suspicion to the shrewd captain's face. He sheathed the knife with a rude laugh. "No, you don't. You're far too valuable alive for me to allow your hands on my knife."

Pocahontas clenched her hands behind her back and smiled in contempt. "King Powhatan will punish you

"ANY MAN WHO TOUCHES YOU WILL FEEL THE EDGE OF MY BLADE!"

for this." She waved toward the forested shore. "If you free me now, I will tell my father I willingly came aboard your ship, for I did. I will say nothing of being held prisoner."

He stared. Admiration for her courage shone in his eyes. "Do you think now that I have you, I'll let you go? Or that I'd believe you'd keep your word?"

Pocahontas set her lips in a line straighter than the crow flies. "Pocahontas does not lie." She turned and proudly walked away. One day, the captain would pay for his wickedness. In the meantime, she would watch and be ready. Surely a way of escape would open before her. *Great Hare,* she silently prayed. *Cast a spell on this man and all those who are Powhatan's enemies.* The words rang hollow in her heart. Who was she to think the Great Hare would stoop to take notice of her plight?

Pocahontas remembered something Reverend Hunt

"GREAT HARE, CAST A SPELL ON THIS MAN. . . !"

had said long ago. "God loves every person who ever lived or ever will. . .so much He sent His only Son to die, so we might live. . .He is another Father."

Would that God hear the prayers of a captive Indian princess? If only John Smith had not gone! Pocahontas felt the familiar stone in her heart that came when she thought of the white man she once saved. When she asked Argall about him, the captain bluntly said John Smith had died long ago. Why, then, did she continue to cling to the hope that he was wrong?

Argall gruffly told her, "You'll be released soon. The minute we reach Jamestown, messengers will run like the wind. All Powhatan has to do is give back the guns and captives he took and agree to peace."

"All?" Pocahontas snorted. "Those are hard terms."

Argall's voice hardened. "Too hard for the return of the daughter he loves?"

Pocahontas said no more. Never in a million years

"HA! JOHN SMITH DIED LONG AGO!"

would the captain or most of the colonists understand Indians and Indian ways. She continued to seek a way of escape but none opened. Things became doubly hard when shortly after they sailed into Jamestown, the leaders declared she could not stay there.

"We are going to send you up the river to Rock Hall," Governor Gates told her. "It is a hundred-acre parsonage across from Henrico." He didn't tell her the five forts in the area would better guard against a Powhatan rescue party, but she knew. Nothing the white men did escaped the attention of the Indians whose land they had stolen.

"Reverend Alexander Whitaker is a fine Christian man," Gates continued. "He will tell you of the one true God. He came to Virginia to teach the tribes about God and make Christians of them."

Pocahontas did not let the little thrill of excitement she felt show, even when she asked, "Does this man

JAMESTOWN'S LEADERS SAID THAT SHE COULD NOT STAY.

have a Holy Bible?"

"Of course, he has a Bible," Gates snapped. "He's a minister, isn't he?" He waved her away but not before she saw the look in his face. Here was another who considered her dull and stupid because of her brown skin. She laughed to herself. Until Powhatan came for her, she would learn the white man's ways and of his God. Perhaps this Reverend Whitaker would teach her to read, or at least tell her more about the little black soldiers that marched across the pages of the Holy Bible.

From the moment Pocahontas reached Rock Hall in the spring of 1613, a new life began. The women of Reverend Whitaker's church took her in hand. Kind but insistent, they clucked and chattered. "Child, for you are a child in spite of having been married, we must get rid of your Indian clothing."

Pocahontas looked from her soft buckskins and

THE WOMEN OF REVEREND WHITAKER'S CHURCH
TOOK HER IN HAND.

moccasins to the tight dresses and high ruffled collars that held the women's necks straight. She looked at their hard leather shoes. "Must I?"

"Yes. You are to be a Christian, you know. You must dress like one and not like a heathen."

"Does your God care about how we dress?"

The ladies looked shocked and giggled behind their hands. An older woman frowned at them. "English ladies always dress properly," she explained.

Pocahontas gave in. She learned to take tiny steps because of the tight shoes and dresses that squeezed her. No longer could she run and fling her arms toward the morning sun. Days became weeks. Weeks became months. Her gaze darted from east to west, north to south whenever she was allowed outside. Surely a rescue party would come soon. Tired of the white man's clothing and ways, she longed to wear her Indian clothing and turn cartwheels in the streets.

SHE LEARNED TO TAKE SMALL STEPS IN THE TIGHT SHOES.

She thought how shocked the good ladies of Rock Hall would look if she did such a thing—and laughed.

"'Twouldn't be lady-like," she mimicked the phrase they flung at her every time she strayed from the path in which they tried to lead her.

Why did Powhatan not come? He had once sent his daughter with the gift of a deer to secure the release of John Smith's captives. Discouraged and weary, Pocahontas lay sleepless night after night and lost much of the sparkle that had been a part of her charm.

Three long months of captivity limped by. At last Powhatan sent an answer to the demand for ransom. "Powhatan wants his daughter," the message said. "However, he cannot send the guns. All but a few were stolen and those that were not are broken. I send them and some English captives to you. The day Pocahontas returns to her father is the day I send 500 bushels of corn and make peace with the white men."

POCAHONTAS LAY SLEEPLESS NIGHT AFTER NIGHT.

Neither Pocahontas nor the English believed the fantastic story about the guns. Pain filled her heart. She had thought Powhatan loved her beyond life. Now he offered a few broken guns for her freedom! Red spots flared in her smooth cheeks. Such a thing insulted her royal blood. Her father's love for the guns she knew he had hidden must be greater than his love for her. Must she remain a prisoner forever? She would rather die.

Lonely and more miserable than she had been in her entire life, Pocahontas remembered her vow to learn more about the white man's God. Until now, she had merely been waiting for the day she could put on her beloved buckskins and moccasins and walk into the forest, free as the eagle that soared over Rock Hall.

"The Great Hare has done nothing," she told herself. "Will the God of the Holy Bible who whispers to

MUST SHE REMAIN A PRISONER FOREVER?

His children's hearts hear my prayers?"

Reverend Whitaker found real interest in his teachings where before Pocahontas had simply listened. Now she questioned him. She drank in the stories from the Bible as a thirsty traveler drinks water from a clear stream. She learned of God and His Son Jesus. She learned how the only way to escape punishment for sin was to trust in Jesus and claim God's promises. The young minister taught her how strong Satan—the devil—was and that there was no place in the Christian religion for casting spells and doing magic.

Many times Pocahontas felt torn between all she heard and everything she knew as a Powhatan princess. Once she said, "This is what John Smith believed. If he truly is dead, is he in heaven? If I become a Christian, will I one day go there and see him again?"

"Of course. That is why I came to Virginia, so those who don't know about God and Christ might learn

POCAHONTAS LEARNED OF GOD AND HIS SON JESUS.

and have a place in heaven," the minister said.

Pocahontas didn't answer, but she started praying for God to let her know if all the things Reverend Whitaker told her were true.

God soon answered the captive's prayers, in a way that forever changed her life.

POCAHONTAS STARTED PRAYING TO GOD.

JOHN ROLFE WAS AS LONELY AS POCAHONTAS.

9
God's Answer

Pocahontas wasn't the only lonely person at Rock Hall. John Rolfe, already well into his experiments with tobacco, felt adrift. His wife had died not long after she'd come to Jamestown and his baby daughter had died in Bermuda. Now twenty-eight, he wondered if he must spend the rest of his life alone.

When Pocahontas was brought to the parsonage as a captive, she stirred Rolfe's interest. He volunteered to help her learn to speak English better. He read to her from the Bible. Her shining dark gaze never left his face, and he thrilled. Yet the growing fondness he felt for her also troubled him. Did not the very Bible from which he taught Pocahontas warn Christians never to join their lives with unbelievers?

A sincere man, John searched his heart. He prayed often, asking for God's guidance. How could he, a man who followed God's laws to the best of his ability, care for a barbarian who worshiped the spirits of animals? Yet as time passed, he saw a change in the Indian girl he helped teach.

He joyously caught the gladness that brightened her face when he came. His heart pounded. Was "Frisky," as he called her, learning to care? He rejoiced even more when she pelted him with questions about God the way hail beats on hard clay ground. If she were to turn from her Indian gods and invite Christ into her heart, he would accept it as a sign of God's will that they marry.

Pocahontas continued to study. She hid the secret love for John Rolfe growing inside her. A year after she had been taken captive, Powhatan still had not come for her. On a beautiful spring day in 1614, she declared the gods of the Powhatan to be false, was

SHE DECLARED THE GODS OF POWHATAN TO BE FALSE.

baptized, and became a Christian. If part of her died at the giving up of all she had once held dear, the look in John Rolfe's face offered her new life.

The English gave her a new name. "You shall be called Rebekah, after the maiden in the Bible who left her people to dwell with her husband Isaac," they told her.

Pocahontas smiled. Peace filled her, the peace she had longed for. It did not remain long. When John Rolfe asked permission to marry Pocahontas, Sir Thomas Dale seized the opportunity to get the guns he knew Powhatan still possessed. He bundled Pocahontas onto a ship and sailed up the river with 150 strong men. He sent word ahead that he would wipe out any who stood in his way. Some Indians answered with a rain of arrows. Dale got even by destroying their villages.

At last the day for which she had waited too long arrived. Her brothers came to Dale's ship. Instead of

POCAHONTAS WAS BROUGHT UP RIVER BY SHIP.

a beaten captive, they found a fine lady dressed in English clothes. She cried, "I waited and waited! Powhatan loved his guns more than his daughter. Now I shall be the wife of John Rolfe and abide with him." She sailed back to Jamestown thinking she would never see her family again. Her father would never forgive her. Only the love in her heart for John Rolfe kept her from despair.

Powhatan amazed everyone. All these months he had clung to the guns through pride and the fear that if he returned them, his tribes would think their king weak. Suddenly everything had changed. Pocahontas was no longer a hostage. He had no need to lose face with a peace offer. "The marriage of my daughter to an Englishman shows friendship between the races," he said in a message. He added, "I vowed never again to enter an English settlement. I cannot break that vow, even to see Pocahontas married. My brother will come."

"POWHATAN LOVED HIS GUNS MORE THAN HIS DAUGHTER."

April 5, 1614, came. Pocahontas stood in the Jamestown church, the object of much attention. Those of her family who came gasped. Could this be the daughter of Powhatan, this woman clad in a long dress, veil, and the string of freshwater pearls her father had sent along with the gift of much land?

At the end of the ceremony, her new husband whispered, "You are now an Englishwoman, Mrs. Rolfe."

For a quick moment, the people around her faded, even John. Tears stung Pocahontas's eyes at the thought of another John. *How proud Captain John Smith would be if he could know.*

The wedding of Pocahontas-Rebekah and John Rolfe began a time known as the Peace of Pocahontas. The settlers marveled that one event could make such a difference. No longer did they fear to leave the fort. Gone were the roving bands of Indians that had plagued them for years. Thickets were simply thickets rather than hiding places for strong-armed war-

THE WEDDING BEGAN A TIME KNOWN AS
"THE PEACE OF POCAHONTAS."

riors with long bows and deadly arrows.

A year later, Pocahontas looked into the face of her tiny, newborn son. Joy filled her heart. How good God was to have given her a loving husband and this precious son! She closed her eyes and whispered a prayer of thanks. Not just for her own happiness but for the continuing peace. Again she thought, *I wish John Smith could know.* . . .

The English people had followed the story of John Rolfe's marriage to an Indian princess with great interest. They were equally excited when they learned of the birth of the Rolfes' son Thomas. Yet they found it hard to understand why huge amounts of money didn't come back to England now that there was peace. All they heard from Virginia were excuses.

Sir Thomas Dale had a bright idea. When he sailed for England in the spring of 1616, why not take John, Pocahontas, and Thomas with him? London would go wild over having a real Indian princess visit, espe-

POCAHONTAS LOOKED INTO THE FACE OF HER NEWBORN SON.

cially one who had forsaken her beliefs and become a Christian. She'd be better than a circus.

Pocahontas thrilled when her husband bounded in with Dale's plan. "I, go to England?" It was beyond her wildest dreams. To see the country from which the coat-wearing people had come and the wonders Namontack had told after his visit. Her eyes glistened, then she looked at small Thomas.

"We will need a nurse," John said. "A good round dozen of your tribe will also go with us. You are a princess, you know, and must travel like one."

Pocahontas felt a pang. Long ago she and Matachanna had talked of the land across the wide, deep waters. If only—

"John," she burst out. "Will you do something for me?"

He looked surprised, but nodded.

"Send a message for Matachanna to come to me." She mysteriously refused to say any more, but ran to

"SEND A MESSAGE FOR MATACHANNA TO COME TO ME. . . ."

her sister when Matachanna arrived. "We are going to England," she cried.

Matachanna looked at Pocahontas as if she were a crazy loon who called by a lake. "England?" Disbelief showed in the face she made.

"Yes. You promised." Pocahontas's eyes sparkled with mischief.

"I never promised to go to England with you," her sister protested, raising her hands in the air at the very suggestion.

"Yes, you did. Remember the day we raced, after the dance of the unmarried girls?"

"Yes. I hurt my foot and you gave up winning to help me." Matachanna still looked puzzled.

"You were so grateful you said, 'One day I will care for you. But not until I no longer hop on one foot—'"

"'—with the other in the air like a long-legged marsh bird fishing for his supper,'" Matachanna quickly finished. They giggled like the sisters they had

"YOU SAID, 'ONE DAY I WILL CARE FOR YOU.'"

been before time and circumstances had sent them in separate ways.

"You no longer hop, and I need you." A poignant light stole into Pocahontas's face. "Not to care for me, but to nurse little Thomas. John says I must spend much time with lords and ladies. Thomas is my life, Matachanna. Will you not go with me and care for him, as I myself would do?"

Matachanna's black eyes moistened. She laid a shapely brown hand on her sister's. "I will go."

They set sail in April and reached an England on fire with curiosity, but no more eager than Pocahontas, her sister, and fellow tribesmen. Nothing in their experience could have made them believe such places existed. Horses and carriages by the score. Vendors shouting their wares in the streets. The noise hurt ears used to forest silences. Even the shrieks of the various Indian dances couldn't compare with the din of London.

Great joy came to Pocahontas soon after she ar-

INDIAN SHRIEKS COULD NOT COMPARE
TO THE DIN OF LONDON.

rived, news that made her forget the strangeness of this far-off country. John Smith was not only alive but in London, back from one of his explorations!

With the city crying out news of Pocahontas and her doings, John must know she was there. Yet parties and balls in her honor followed one another, and he made no effort to come see her. Lady De La Warre made herself responsible for the Indian princess as far as correct clothing and manners. Pocahontas's own natural dignity served her well. She sailed through her many social duties, even meeting the king and queen.

Once the newness wore off, she treasured most her times at home. As in the olden days, she faithfully reported all she saw and heard to Matachanna, giggling and poking fun at the stuffy English airs some of the people put on. She often sadly wondered why John Smith never came to see her. She considered calling on him but proudly shook her head. *Nay.* If he had forgotten the Indian girl who had saved his life, so be it. She would not be the one to remind him.

LADY DE LA WARRE TAUGHT HER CORRECT MANNERS.

THE ROLFES TOOK A SMALL HOUSE IN THE COUNTRY.

10
The Last Voyage

The air of London was not good for the Indians, so the Rolfes took a small house in the country. Pocahontas loved it and longed to stay. John said no. Secretary of the colony, he wanted to rush back to Jamestown and grow bigger tobacco crops. He painted bright pictures of converting Indians by the hundreds.

Such talk saddened Pocahontas. Her people clung to their beliefs just as the English did to theirs. It would be no easy task to replace the heathen gods with Christianity, if indeed it could be done at all. Sometimes she felt like a wishbone, pulled by love of her people and love for her English husband.

The early months of 1617 brought gales to England. Pocahontas gave thanks. She and her party could not sail in such winds. Even though the warm, damp weather made her cough, she still wanted to stay in England. Peace between the whites and Indians continued, but war was inevitable. Powhatan was an old man. Soon he would be no more. Another would rule—perhaps a hot-blooded chief who hated the English and was determined to drive them out of Virginia forever. Pocahontas could not bear to think of it.

One of the Indians who came to England with Pocahontas openly rejoiced. Powhatan had sent Tomocomo along in order to report on England, its royalty, and the God of the white people. He also told Tomocomo to count the people. Tomocomo little resembled Namontack, who had been so impressed with the tall, stone buildings and crowds of people that he had noticed little else!

Tomocomo hated everything he discovered in and about England: clanging church bells, so many people he could barely count even a small part of them, streets

TOMOCOMO HATED EVERYTHING ABOUT ENGLAND AND ITS PEOPLE.

that stank, and buildings crowded together until a man thought he would die from his longing to be free. Tomocomo marched through the days, living for the time he could go home to the Powhatan kingdom with its clear waters and clean air. He refused to wear English clothes.

"Pah!" If the English did not like his Indian clothing, his painted face, and feathers, neither did he like their ways. His black eyes gleamed with spite. The English king he dismissed with a wave of the hand. "That small, pale-faced man a *king?*" Tomocomo snorted. "Not even a dog of Powhatan's would consent to be ruled by the weakling who sits on the throne in this strange country."

Remembering Powhatan's orders, Tomocomo gained audience with the bishop of London to find out about the English religion. Sir Thomas Dale interpreted. The Bishop came off second best, in spite of his flow of explanation. Once Tomocomo learned

TOMOCOMO'S BLACK EYES GLEAMED WITH SPITE.

there was not even a picture of the English God, he didn't care to hear more. Besides, the white God hadn't kept the whites from lying, had He? Everyone knew John Smith hadn't died, as the Jamestown colonists said.

"Tomocomo wishes John Smith *had* died," the Indian muttered. A deep scowl turned his face ugly. "He called Powhatan friend and brother. Yet John Smith does not come to bring the daughter of our chief a gift of welcome. Pah!" Tomocomo spat on the ground, as if to rid himself of the very taste of England and everything in it.

Pocahontas often thought the same thing. It saddened her. She had been in England almost a year and still John Smith had not sought her out. "He will not come now," she told herself. "I must forget him."

Pocahontas was wrong. Not long afterward, Smith traveled up the Thames River with some friends and came to call. At first, all she could feel was anger at

POCAHONTAS OFTEN THOUGHT OF JOHN SMITH.

having been ignored. Then memories came, so strong it took a long time before she could even ask why he had stayed away. He mumbled some excuse, but she would have none of it.

"Did not Pocahontas lay her own head on yours when Powhatan wished to kill you?" the Indian princess cried. "Did she not bring much food so you and your people would not starve?" She crossed her arms in the same haughty manner her father did when challenged. "I knew not that you lived. Everyone in Jamestown said you were dead." Her voice rose and grew shrill. "Only when I came to this land did I learn you lived. The heart of Pocahontas leaped within her. Ah, she sang like the birds in the trees. Soon she would see her friend."

Smith's face reddened, and he looked down.

"All of England has welcomed me," Pocahontas told him. "All except the one I knew would rush to me like the rivers freed from ice when he learned I

"EVERYONE IN JAMESTOWN SAID YOU WERE DEAD!"

had become English through marriage."

After a time of stumbling conversation, Pocahontas told her caller she would forever be his countryman, then sadly watched him leave her home. Weary to the point of no longer caring for anything except to rest, she sought her couch in hopes of finding sleep. Instead, the past and present blended into torture. "I wish he had not come at all," she whispered, but her heart denied it. Something inside told her she would gaze no more in this life on the one who had changed the course of her own life so much.

Pocahontas continued to cough. It weakened her. She did not complain to her husband, but hoped and prayed he would change his mind about returning to America. Caught up in his own affairs, John Rolfe continued to plan for their departure. A strong woman, she knew she must obey her husband's commands.

The wind lessened at last. Pocahontas, Matachanna, young Thomas, and Tomocomo went to London and

"I WISH HE HAD NOT COME AT ALL...."

boarded Samuel Argall's ship, the *George*. Her mind raced back to the day just four years earlier when she had boarded a ship commanded by Argall. The same feeling of helplessness that had attacked her then now swept through her weakened body. She stumbled and had to be helped to her quarters. She couldn't bear to look back at the city that had opened wide its arms to an Indian princess.

Long before the ship left the river and sailed into the sea, Pocahontas knew how sick she really was. "Take me ashore," she pleaded. "I cannot go on."

Her shadowed eyes and blanched face at last tore John Rolfe's thoughts from his mighty plans about conquering Virginia for God to the woman he loved. How could he have been such a fool? Even eyes turned toward America should have seen how Pocahontas had failed. She was dying before him.

"Drop anchor," he pleaded with Captain Argall. "We must get help for her." He knew as he spoke, it

POCAHONTAS KNEW HOW SICK SHE REALLY WAS.

was too late.

The physician who came examined Pocahontas. He gravely shook his head and called Rolfe aside. "I can do nothing. She is too far gone."

"God forgive me." John Rolfe left the doctor and knelt by his wife's side. His shoulders heaved, and he buried his face in his arms.

"Do not grieve, husband." Pocahontas lifted a thin hand and placed it on the bowed head. "All must die. Those who believe have nothing to fear. We know we shall meet again." Her voice softened. "Take good care of our son. Teach him to do good and work for peace. He carries the blood of two great nations in his small body."

She paused, then went on. "I could not tell you how much I dreaded taking the long voyage home. I fear what may come. When you see my father, tell him I lie in a land where I found much happiness."

Again, Pocahontas hesitated. "All my life I have

"DO NOT GRIEVE, HUSBAND, ALL MUST DIE. . . ."

wanted to know what lay across the sea, behind the mountains, and over the horizon." A smile blossomed. For a moment she looked young as the girl who had danced and laughed and sang, the girl who had risked her father's anger to save John Smith. "Now I take my last voyage. I will be waiting when you and Thomas come." The dark eyes that had seen war and peace, famine and plenty, sunshine and storm for a short twenty-one years closed.

"NOW I WILL TAKE MY LAST VOYAGE. . . :"

OLD KING POWHATAN MOURNED THE DEATH OF POCAHONTAS.

Afterword

Broken-hearted from the loss of his second wife, John Rolfe sailed back to America. He left behind his two-year-old son Thomas. The child was not well enough to travel after his mother's death and burial. Thomas lived with his father's brother until he reached manhood and then became an important person in Virginia.

Other things changed. The Peace of Pocahontas held for a time, but, even as Pocahontas had feared, the English rushed headlong into trouble in their attempts to convert the Indians. Old King Powhatan mourned the death of the daughter who had been dearer than life to him. He died in 1618, still true to his Indian gods, as were all but a small part of the Indians.

Powhatan's brother, Opechancanough, became chief of the Powhatan nation. He strutted like a turkey with ruffled feathers, lived in an English-style house, and lorded it over his subjects. He pretended friendliness with the settlers and secretly plotted their destruction.

John Rolfe died just a few days before a surprise attack in March, 1622. More than 350 whites were killed. The battle ended the Peace of Pocahontas. War continued until the coat-wearing people and their sticks that shot thunder instead of arrows drove the Indians farther and farther away.

John Smith died in England at the age of fifty-one, but stories of his bravery and the courageous Indian maiden Pocahontas who accepted Christ and longed for peace will never die.

PRUDENCE

OF
PLYMOUTH
PLANTATION

AT A CHRISTIAN BOOKSTORE NEAR YOU!

AWESOME BOOKS FOR KIDS!

The Young Reader's Christian Library
Action, Adventure, and Fun Reading!

This series for young readers ages 8 to 12 is action-packed, fast-paced, and Christ-centered! With exciting illustrations on every other page following the text, kids won't be able to put these books down! Over 100 illustrations per book. All books are paperbound. The unique size (4 3/16" x 5 3/8") makes these books easy to take anywhere!

A Great Selection to Satisfy All Kids!

Abraham Lincoln	In His Steps	Prudence of Plymouth
Ben-Hur	Jesus	Plantation
Billy Sunday	Joseph	Robinson Crusoe
Christopher Columbus	Lydia	Roger Williams
Corrie ten Boom	Miriam	Ruth
David Livingstone	Paul	Samuel Morris
Deborah	Peter	The Swiss Family
Elijah	The Pilgrim's Progress	Robinson
Esther	Pocahontas	Taming the Land
Heidi	Pollyanna	Thunder in the Valley
Hudson Taylor		Wagons West

Available wherever books are sold.
Or order from: Barbour Publishing, Inc., P.O. Box 719
Uhrichsville, Ohio 44683
http://www.barbourbooks.com

$2.50 each retail, plus $1.00 for postage and handling per order. Prices subject to change without notic